Verbal Reasoning
& Comprehension

The 11+ Practice Book

with Assessment Tests

For the CEM (Durham University) test

Ages
7-8

Practise • Prepare • Pass
Everything your child needs for 11+ success

How to use this Practice Book

This book is divided into two parts — themed question practice and assessment tests.
There are answers with detailed explanations in the pull-out answer book.

Themed question practice

- Each page has practice questions on a different theme. Use these pages to work out your child's strengths and the areas they find tricky.

- The questions get harder down each page.

Assessment tests

- The second half of the book contains eight assessment tests, each with a mix of question types from the first half of the book.

- If you want to give your child timed practice, give them a time limit of 20 minutes for each test, and ask them to work as quickly and carefully as they can.

- The tests get harder from 1-8, so don't be surprised if your child finds the later ones more tricky.

- Your child should aim for a mark of around 85% (30 questions correct) in each test. If they score less than this, use their results to work out the areas they need more practice on.

- If they haven't managed to finish the test in time, they need to work on increasing their speed, whereas if they have made a lot of mistakes, they need to work more carefully.

- Keep track of your child's scores using the progress chart on the inside back cover of the book.

- This book gives your child intensive practice of the Verbal Reasoning sections of the test. There will be other elements on the real 11+ test, such as Maths and Non-Verbal Reasoning.

- Although our question types are based on those set by CEM, we cannot guarantee that your child's actual 11+ exam will take the same format or contain the same question types as this book.

Published by CGP

Editors:
Claire Boulter, Holly Poynton

Contributors:
Steve Martin, Alison Mott, Julie Moxon

With thanks to Glenn Rogers and Lucy Towle for the proofreading.

Please note that CGP is not associated with CEM or The University of Durham in any way. This book does not include any official questions and it is not endorsed by CEM or The University of Durham.

CEM, Centre for Evaluation and Monitoring, Durham University and *The University of Durham* are all trademarks of The University of Durham.

ISBN: 978 1 84762 571 7
www.cgpbooks.co.uk
Printed by Elanders Ltd, Newcastle upon Tyne
Clipart from Corel®

Based on the classic CGP style created by Richard Parsons.

CONTENTS

Plurals

Plurals

Write the correct plural of the word in brackets. Look at this example:

Mira and I watched five _____*films*_____ (**film**).

1. Three _____ (**girl**) were chosen to carry the flag in the ceremony.

2. The shoes were stacked in _____ (**box**) on the shelves.

3. We cleaned up the _____ (**ash**) from the bonfire.

4. My brother has three pairs of _____ (**glass**) because he always loses them.

5. When we go on holiday, I like eating _____ (**peach**) for breakfast.

6. I blew out the candles on the cake and I made two _____ (**wish**).

/ 6

Plurals

Underline the correct plural from the brackets to complete the sentence. Look at this example:

The (**babys** **babies**) were crying because of the loud noise.

*Hint: If there's a consonant before the 'y', drop the 'y' and add 'ies'
to make the plural. If there's a vowel before the 'y', just add 's'.*

7. Gemma told the (**boys** **boyes**) to stop being naughty.

8. The river met at the bottom of three (**vallies** **valleys**).

9. All the (**jellies** **jellys**) slid off the table and onto the floor.

10. We couldn't decide which of the (**puppys** **puppies**) we wanted to take home.

11. Shing looked across at the (**chimneys** **chimnies**) on the roof.

/ 6

12. There were three (**flys** **flies**) caught in the spider's web.

Homophones

Homophones

Choose the correct homophone from the brackets.
Look at this example:

> I have ____to____ (to two too) go to rugby practice now.

Hint: Homophones are words that sound the same but mean different things.

1. Ow! This soup is _____ (to two too) hot.

2. Jamila owns _____ (to two too) pet rabbits.

3. I can't go in because the ghost is _____ (to two too) scary.

4. Can we go _____ (to two too) the cinema instead?

/ 4

5. Can I have another _____ (piece peace) of cake?

6. Granny told us to go upstairs so she could get some _____ (piece peace).

7. Luckily, the plate stayed all in one _____ (piece peace).

8. Now we can have dinner in _____ (piece peace).

/ 4

9. Tolek and Sam have lost _____ (they're their there) coats.

10. I wonder whether _____ (they're their there) hats will blow off.

11. Look at my gerbils — _____ (they're their there) so cute!

12. Dad has parked the car over _____ (they're their there).

/ 4

Prefixes and Suffixes

Suffixes

Add the suffix **ness** or **ship** to complete the word in bold.
Look at this example:

Your **kind**___ness___ to me has been wonderful.

1. I had caught an **ill**_____ which made my ears turn purple.

2. Even though we argue, my sister and I have a good **relation**_____.

3. I've started going rollerblading to improve my **fit**_____.

4. The parents questioned the **fair**_____ of the class test.

5. Amanda has a gym **member**_____ which she never uses.

6. Flavel and Gregson are a perfect ice-skating **partner**_____.

/ 6

*Hint: Prefixes and suffixes are groups of letters that can be added
to the beginning or end of a word to change its meaning.*

Prefixes

Add the prefix **dis**, **im** or **un** to complete the word in bold.
Look at this example:

The banana-shaped hammer was quite ___im___**practical**.

7. There was an _____**pleasant** smell coming from the hallway.

8. Hadi and I _____**agreed** on what the best pudding would be.

9. I was so excited to _____**wrap** the presents.

*Hint: Read the word in bold
with 'dis', 'im' and 'un' in front
and see which sounds best.*

10. Sometimes my P.E. kit just seems to _____**appear**.

11. The scarf was _____**perfect** because I lost count when I was knitting it.

/ 6

12. The 1,000 piece jigsaw puzzle seemed _____**possible** to complete.

Awkward Spellings

Vowels

Underline the correct word from the brackets to complete each sentence. Look at this example:

> The cows had escaped from the (feild <u>field</u>).

Hint: Remember the rule — 'i before e, except after c, but only when it rhymes with bee', but don't forget that there are a few words that don't follow this rule.

1. They found an ancient Roman **(shield sheild)** in the ground.

2. Swimming 30 lengths of the pool was a great **(achievement acheivement)**.

3. Aunty Ellen wrote me a **(breif brief)** note to go with the recipe she sent.

4. The **(ceiling cieling)** was covered in pink goo after the pudding exploded.

5. Kushi loves **(science sceince)** because she thinks experiments are fun.

6. I have a **(neice niece)** called Ruthie who likes to run around.

/ 6

Consonants

Underline the correct word from the brackets to complete each sentence. Look at this example:

> You need a (sadle <u>saddle</u>) to ride a horse.

7. Grey **(squirrels squirels)** are more common than red ones.

8. Maurice was trying to stop **(biting bitting)** his nails.

9. Look at those **(bubles bubbles)** coming out of the bathroom.

10. I don't like going **(running runing)** in the rain.

11. Nora **(waddles wadles)** like a duck when she walks.

12. We were **(hopping hoping)** the film would finish before bedtime.

/ 6

Section One — Spelling and Grammar

Mixed Spelling Questions

Underline the correct word to complete each sentence.
Look at this example:

> I was **(shakking <u>shaking</u>)** with nerves before I got up to sing.

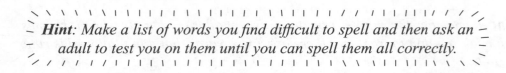

Hint: Make a list of words you find difficult to spell and then ask an adult to test you on them until you can spell them all correctly.

1. I was so **(dishappy unhappy)** when the cricket match was cancelled.

2. We knew the address was **(correct corect)** because Minna had written it out for us.

3. There were **(ditches ditchs)** on both sides of the track.

4. Suni had a really **(wierd weird)** dream about raccoons.

/ 4

5. Kevin is **(hidding hiding)** behind the armchair.

6. The **(keys keyes)** for our cottage were left under a flowerpot.

7. Uncle Niito taught me how to make shadow **(pupets puppets)**.

/ 4

8. I always try to be **(cheerful cheerfull)**, even if I feel grumpy.

9. **(Tomorow Tomorrow)** evening is the final of the cooking challenge.

10. I waited **(impatiently unpatiently)** for the plums to ripen.

11. The **(skies skys)** over the countryside are often blue.

/ 4

12. Gareth walked his dog around the **(feilds fields)** before breakfast.

Mixed Spelling Questions

Underline the word that contains a spelling mistake in each line.
Look at this example:

> Jenna is <u>runing</u> a marathon next week.

1. My freind Leila has beautiful dark hair.

2. We did all the activitys on offer.

3. Miles has court the measles.

4. I went to the shop to by some sweets.

5. My mum always wants to put ribons in my hair.

6. Callum hated it when his bedroom was distidy.

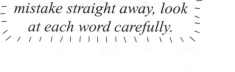

Hint: If you can't spot the mistake straight away, look at each word carefully.

/ 6

Each sentence contains a spelling mistake. Underline the word with the error and write the correct spelling on the line.
Look at this example:

> The tiger <u>chassed</u> after the monkey. _____chased_____

7. I had hidden Mohab's pensil under the table. _____

8. My uncle Mark is always very joly at Christmas. _____

9. She pulled a small peice of paper out of the hat. _____

10. Tina was only pasing through, so she didn't stay. _____

11. The trees were bear — all their leaves had fallen. _____

12. We all carried torchs in the Bonfire Night parade. _____

/ 6

Verts

Verbs

For each sentence rewrite the verb in bold in the present tense.
Look at this example:

> Hari **got** home late from school. ___gets___

1. I **dressed** my little sister in a red jumper. _____

2. My friends **were** all taller than me. _____

3. John **had** never been to the seaside before. _____

4. My pet frog Hoppy **jumped** really high. _____

5. He **knew** how to do this question. _____

6. The children **talked** during every lesson. _____

Hint: The present tense describes something that is happening now.

/ 6

Verbs

Underline the correct form of the verb to make the sentence past tense.
Look at this example:

> Fatima **(hopes hoped hope)** the test wouldn't be too hard.

7. Bettina **(loved love loves)** her brand-new purple shoes.

8. I **(go goes went)** home early because I was ill.

9. My uncle was **(blew blown blows)** down by the helicopter.

10. Naseem **(buy buys bought)** some new watercolour paints.

11. Gemma **(takes took take)** the bus to school today.

12. The flock of geese has **(flew flying flown)** into the air.

/ 6

Section One — Spelling and Grammar

Verbs and Connectives

Verbs

For each sentence rewrite the verb in bold in the past tense.
Look at this example:

> Jan **plays** the flute really well. ___played___

Hint: Often you add '-ed' to the end of a verb to make it past tense, but watch out for verbs where you have to do something different.

1. I **decide** to try the blueberry ice cream. _____

2. We **drink** lemonade during the summer holidays. _____

3. The fat duck **breaks** the ice in the pond. _____

4. Daniel **throws** the beanbag high in the air. _____

5. Kiri **catches** the ball easily with one hand. _____

6. I **think** I would like to be an actor. _____

/ 6

Connectives

Underline the correct connective from the brackets to complete each sentence. Look at this example:

> I fell over **(if <u>and</u>)** grazed my knee.

Hint: A connective is a word that joins two parts of a sentence together.

7. Tara can run fast, **(but also)** she's not good at climbing trees.

8. I finished my story, **(if so)** I was allowed to play outside.

9. I will eat my peas first, **(while then)** I will eat my mashed potatoes.

10. Marcus won't join the choir **(or but)** the ballroom dancing club.

11. I want to be a vet **(because except)** I love animals.

12. Kieran will come over **(also unless)** he's busy.

/ 6

Mixed Grammar Questions

Each sentence has one grammatical error. Underline the word which is wrong and write the correct word on the line. Look at this example:

> I <u>makes</u> a rope swing yesterday.   <u>made</u>

1. The squirrel get stuck in the fence yesterday. _____

2. I be going to France next Tuesday. _____

3. Iestyn doesn't have no pets. _____

4. Alex eat a toffee apple last night. _____

5. Me am not scared of ghosts. _____

6. Yuni can run fastest than Seb. _____

/ 6

Hint: If you get stuck, try reading the sentence out loud.

Underline the correct word from the brackets to complete each sentence. Look at this example:

> Katie (**jump** <u>**jumps**</u> **jumping**) in puddles all the time.

7. Harry (**has have had**) a pet snake when he was five.

8. Kirstie is the (**tall taller tallest**) girl in the whole class.

9. The enormous elephant (**was were am**) walking towards us.

10. Come and see (**us they we**) when you get home.

11. Ashwin liked all vegetables (**unless except although**) cauliflower.

/ 6

12. Eloise wants to (**write wrote written**) a book about dragons.

Odd One Out

Three of the words in each list are linked.
Underline the word that is **not** related to the other three.
Look at this example:

cat   dog   hamster   <u>shark</u>

1. pen   blue   black   white

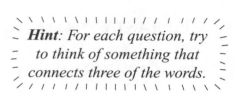

Hint: For each question, try to think of something that connects three of the words.

2. weep   cry   happy   sob

3. grass   plant   owl   tree

/ 4

4. pillow   blanket   duvet   fridge

5. juice   toast   eggs   bacon

6. run   sleep   skip   jump

7. student   pupil   learner   grandad

/ 4

8. shower   roof   sink   bath

9. shoe   sock   clog   boot

10. zip   buttons   clothes   laces

11. draw   sketch   write   sing

/ 4

12. sit   jump   bounce   leap

Closest Meaning

Underline the word that has the most similar meaning to the word in capital letters.
Look at this example:

RUN	<u>sprint</u>	walk	stroll

1. **TASTY**   eat   food   delicious

2. **CLEVER**   books   smart   school

3. **BAD**   good   naughty   steal

4. **EAT**   chew   meal   plate

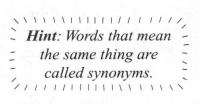

Hint: Words that mean the same thing are called synonyms.

/ 4

5. **LADY**   pretty   woman   duke

6. **WRITE**   ink   scribble   pencil

7. **SLIP**   limp   skid   jig

8. **MAIL**   post   stamp   man

/ 4

9. **POEM**   word   book   rhyme

10. **FRIEND**   person   mate   enemy

11. **KNIFE**   blade   fork   sharp

12. **BATTLE**   soldier   army   fight

/ 4

Closest Meaning

Complete the word on the right so that it means the same,
or nearly the same, as the word on the left.
Look at this example:

| shut | c l o s e |

1. **quick**   f a ☐ t

2. **rock**   ☐ t o n e

3. **see**   l ☐ ☐ k

4. **correct**   r i ☐ ☐ t

> *Hint: If you're not sure how to spell a word, try writing it on scrap paper first.*

/ 4

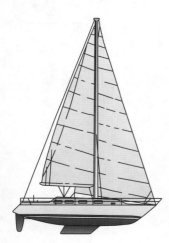

5. **afraid**   s ☐ a r ☐ d

6. **mean**   n ☐ s ☐ y

7. **little**   ☐ m a ☐ l

8. **ship**   b o ☐ ☐

/ 4

9. **easy**   s ☐ m ☐ l e

10. **wet**   d ☐ ☐ p

11. **smell**   ☐ ☐ i n k

12. **glad**   ☐ a p ☐ y

/ 4

Opposite Meaning

Underline the word that has the opposite meaning
to the word in capital letters.
Look at this example:

TINY   <u>big</u>   small   thin

Hint: Words that mean the opposite of each other are called antonyms.

1. **LOTS**   plenty   more   few

2. **OPEN**   wide   closed   near

3. **IN**   under   over   out

4. **DARK**   moon   morning   light

/ 4

5. **FULL**   empty   open   stuffed

6. **SHORT**   small   tall   big

7. **DAY**   sun   night   week

8. **LOUD**   quiet   sing   shout

/ 4

9. **HARD**   soft   tricky   large

10. **CHEAP**   money   free   expensive

11. **LUMPY**   uneven   mashed   smooth

12. **RAW**   fresh   cooked   crunchy

/ 4

Opposite Meaning

Complete the word on the right so that it means the opposite,
or nearly the opposite, of the word on the left.
Look at this example:

up   d o w n

Hint: Think about whether each missing letter is likely to be a vowel or a consonant.

1. **long**   s h o r t

2. **easy**   h a r d

3. **rich**   p o o r

4. **bad**   g o o d

/ 4

5. **pull**   p u s h

6. **throw**   c a t c h

7. **clean**   d i r t y

8. **north**   s o u t h

/ 4

9. **far**   n e a r

10. **ugly**   p r e t t y

11. **above**   b e l o w

12. **float**   s i n k

/ 4

Section Two — Word Meanings

Reorder Words to Make a Sentence

Rearrange the words so that each sentence makes sense.
Underline the word which doesn't fit into the sentence.
Look at this example:

> school I to <u>paper</u> went

The remaining words can be arranged into the sentence:
I went to school.

1. <u>tails</u> my brown is cat

2. clowns <u>nose</u> funny are

3. I potato eats <u>like</u> mashed

4. dog Tony his <u>fetch</u> walked

Hint: Try saying the sentence out loud to help you work out which word doesn't fit.

/ 4

5. flew I <u>storm</u> kite my

6. <u>time</u> mushrooms are some poisonous

7. the <u>scare</u> mouse nibbled cheese the

8. have lobsters claws <u>me</u>

/ 4

9. my scarves knits <u>tea</u> gran

10. I prize first <u>by</u> won

11. I in <u>mistake</u> believe fairies

12. spade your bucket and take <u>sea</u>

/ 4

Related Words

The words in capitals are related in some way. Choose the word from the brackets that fits best with the words in capitals.
Look at this example:

> SNOW HAIL SUN WIND (weather <u>rain</u> wet sky)

Hint: The correct answer will be the same type of word as the words in capitals.

1. KING QUEEN PRINCE DUKE (castle princess royal rich)

2. TENNIS RUGBY FOOTBALL HOCKEY (badminton sport play team)

3. HAT SCARF COAT BOOTS (cold clothes winter gloves)

4. OCEAN LAKE STREAM POND (water wet sea fish)

/ 4

5. DESK TEACHER BOARD BOOK (learn swing computer play)

6. ADD DIVIDE MULTIPLY HALVE (maths numbers calculator subtract)

7. LEG FOOT HAND ARM (neck step man person)

8. FISH PRAWN SHARK SQUID (boat sea jellyfish fin)

/ 4

9. FORK BOWL PLATE KNIFE (dinner spoon eat food)

10. LEMON LIME SATSUMA GRAPEFRUIT (orange yellow citrus fruit)

11. MILK WATER COLA JUICE (drink liquid tea cold)

/ 4

12. PEN CHALK FELT-TIP PENCIL (crayon draw colours mark)

Using Rules of English

> Underline the correct word from the brackets to complete each sentence. Look at this example:
>
> > Ed **(doing <u>does</u> do)** karate every Wednesday night.

1. We are **(go going gone)** to the zoo during the holidays.

2. Anoukh **(left leaving leave)** the tap running, so the bath overflowed.

3. The naughty children thought **(them us they)** had got away with it.

/ 4

4. Simon is the **(quickness quickly fastest)** runner in our class.

5. My house is **(small smaller smallest)** than Heather's.

6. The brass band **(begin began beginning)** to play as we walked along the beach.

7. The sausages **(burns burning burned)** quickly in the frying pan.

/ 4

8. The small boys **(were was where)** shouting loudly and excitedly.

Hint: If you're stuck, try covering the words in turn so you can see which word looks right.

9. Dad wants **(we us our)** to rent a caravan for our next holiday.

10. Granny **(do done did)** not see the cat until she sat on him.

11. I wish Eduardo would tell me where **(he his they)** is going.

/ 4

12. Mum was cross when Tom **(break breaks broke)** her favourite mug.

Choose a Word

Choose the correct word to complete each sentence below.

1. Penguins cannot fly, but they ☐ can ☐ would swim very well.
   ☐ don't

2. Playing netball is good for your coordination and ☐ style ☐ breath . ☐ fitness

/ 3

3. The Scouts were ☐ allowed ☐ moved in 1907 by Robert Baden-Powell.
   ☐ formed

---

4. Tides on Earth are caused by the ☐ laziness ☐ pull of the Sun and the Moon.
   ☐ rest

5. A ☐ healthy ☐ poor diet includes plenty of fruit and vegetables.
   ☐ sickly

6. Every person's fingerprints are ☐ false ☐ unique · ☐ fragile

/ 3

---

7. The ☐ first ☐ last Olympic Games were held in Greece nearly 3000 years ago.
   ☐ only

8. The Vikings explored lots of the world ☐ with ☐ by sea. ☐ on

Hint: Read the sentence with each different option to see which one makes sense.

9. The ☐ larger ☐ large rainforest on Earth is the Amazon rainforest.
   ☐ largest

/ 3

Choose a Word

Choose the correct words to complete each passage below.

Reza stood nervously on stage
1. ☐ waiting
☐ wait   for the curtains to open.
☐ waited

From the school hall she could
2. ☐ see
☐ listen the buzz of conversation as
☐ hear

hundreds of proud parents waited for the pantomime to
3. ☐ halt
☐ begin .
☐ enjoy

/ 3

In 1969, Apollo 11 became the first manned spacecraft to
4. ☐ launch
☐ land   on the Moon.
☐ live

The commander of the spacecraft, Neil Armstrong,
5. ☐ was
☐ were
☐ will

the first man to walk
6. ☐ in
☐ on the Moon.
☐ by

/ 3

Although mainland Britain has four
7. ☐ numbers
☐ lengths of snake, there are no wild snakes
☐ types

in Ireland. Legend has it that Saint Patrick, the patron saint of Ireland,
8. ☐ drove
☐ asked
☐ seen

them all into the sea after they
9. ☐ kicked
☐ left   him.
☐ attacked

/ 3

Section Three — Completing Passages

Fill In Missing Letters

Fill in the missing letters to complete the words in the following sentences.

Hint: Read the sentence and try to work out what the missing word might be before you look at the letters you've been given.

1. Some trees sh☐☐d their leaves in autumn.

2. Twenty thousand years ago, Scotland was cove☐☐d in ice.

3. The capital ☐ity of France is Paris.

4. Cheetahs are the fastest land an☐m☐ls in the world.

/ 4

5. Dinosaurs first appeared ☐ore than 230 million years ago.

6. You must w☐☐r a helmet when you're cycling.

7. The Sahara is the biggest sandy de☐er☐ on the planet.

/ 4

8. People who don't eat meat are ☐alle☐ vegetarians.

9. Lightning oft☐☐ occurs during storms.

10. Bamboo can grow a metre in a s☐☐gle day.

11. Henry VIII was marr☐☐d six times.

/ 4

12. The first steam train was b☐☐lt in 1804.

Fill In Missing Letters

Fill in the missing letters to complete the words in the following passages.

1. Platypuses live in ea[ ]tern Australia.

2. They have a beak, like that of a duck, and web[ ]d feet to help them swim.

3. Unli[ ]e most mammals, they lay eggs.

   When European scientists first saw drawings of the animal,

   they thought that it had been made up

4. bec[ ]se it looked too strange to be real.

/ 4

Hint: Check your spelling carefully with these questions.

5. Ben Nevis is the hi[ ]hest mountain in the British Isles.

   It is located near the town of Fort William in Scotland.

6. Every year, on the first Sat[ ]rday of September, there is a race to the top.

7. Unlike most races, runners have to carry waterproofs, warm clo[ ]es and a

   whistle. This is because the weather can change quickly on the mountain,

8. and anyone with[ ]t the right equipment could be in danger.

/ 4

9. It was still dark when Will woke up, and for a mom[ ]nt he wasn't sure what had

   woken him. Then the sound came again — a loud tap at the window.

10. Will slid out of bed, sh[ ]ver[ ]ng as his feet touched the cold floorboards,

    and crept across the room.

11. Drawing back the curtain, he was surp[ ]ised to see a boy of about

12. his own age stand[ ]g below, just about to throw another pebble.

/ 4

Finding Hidden Facts

Read the information carefully, then use it to answer the question that follows. Write your answer on the line.

Hint: Read the question carefully — sometimes you need to find the person who does the fewest things and sometimes you need to find the person who does the most things.

1. Jill, Katy, Tariq and Mike are playing in the playground.

   Tariq and Mike go on the slide. Mike, Jill and Katy go on the roundabout. Katy and Mike go on the seesaw.

   Who goes on the **most** things?   _____

2. Yosuf, Jeremy, Kyle and Ben are talking about their toys.

   Yosuf and Kyle have bikes. Jeremy and Yosuf have puzzles. Kyle, Ben and Jeremy have yo-yos.

   Who has the **fewest** toys?   _____

3. Claire, Chad, Sam and Guang are talking about which fruits they like.

   Claire and Sam like apples. Chad, Guang and Sam like oranges. Claire, Sam and Chad like pears.

   Who likes the **fewest** fruits?   _____

4. Tiffany, Selena, Luca and Freddie are going to a theme park.

   Tiffany, Selena and Luca want to go on the teacup ride. Freddie and Luca want to go on the roller coaster. Luca and Freddie want to go on the swing boats.

   Who wants to go on the **most** rides?   _____

/ 4

Multiple-Statement Questions — Logic

Read the information carefully, then use it to answer the question that follows. Underline the correct answer.

1. Martia, Phil, Whitney and Olivier all take part in an egg and spoon race. Martia wins. Whitney comes fourth. Olivier comes second. Phil doesn't come last.

   If these statements are true, only one of the sentences below **cannot** be true. Which one?

   A Whitney loses.
   B Phil comes third.
   C Olivier loses.
   D Martia comes first.

   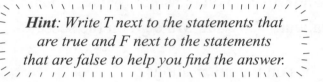
   Hint: Write T next to the statements that are true and F next to the statements that are false to help you find the answer.

2. Fred, Boris, Tina and Dana are talking about which sports they play. Fred and Dana play rugby. Tina and Fred play tennis. Boris only plays cricket. Dana and Tina play squash.

   If these statements are true, only one of the sentences below **cannot** be true. Which one?

   A Tina plays more than one sport.
   B Dana plays rugby and squash.
   C Boris is the only one to play cricket.
   D Boris plays two sports.

3. Richard, Emily, Dre and Meera are raising money for charity. Emily raises twice as much as Meera. Meera raises £10. Richard raises £17. Dre raises £8.

   If these statements are true, only one of the sentences below **must** be true. Which one?

   A Emily raises the most money.
   B Dre raises £7.
   C Emily raises £25.
   D Richard raises the least money.

   / 3

Multiple-Statement Questions — Logic

Read the information carefully, then use it to answer the question that follows. Underline the correct answer.

Hint: Read the question carefully to see whether you need to find what <u>must</u> be true or what <u>cannot</u> be true.

4. Mei, Hugo, Arusi and Daniel are talking about their favourite sandwiches.
Hugo only likes cheese. Daniel and Mei like tuna. Arusi and Daniel like ham.
Mei and Daniel like bacon.

   If these statements are true, only one of the sentences below **cannot** be true. Which one?

   A Daniel likes three types of sandwich.
   B Hugo doesn't like ham.
   C Mei only likes one type of sandwich.
   D Arusi only likes ham.

5. Baruti, Josie, Kirstie and Raj are doing a sponsored walk. Raj walks the furthest.
Josie walks 5 miles. Kirstie walks 2 more miles than Josie. Baruti walks 4 miles.

   If these statements are true, only one of the sentences below **must** be true. Which one?

   A Raj walks 9 miles.
   B Baruti hurts his knee and has to stop.
   C Kirstie walks 6 miles.
   D Josie walks further than Baruti.

6. Aduke, Jen, Sarah and Leigh are having a sleepover. Aduke goes to sleep first. Jen is the last one to go to sleep. Leigh goes to sleep at midnight. Sarah goes to sleep at 1 o'clock.

   If these statements are true, only one of the sentences below **must** be true. Which one?

   A Aduke goes to sleep at 11 o'clock.
   B Leigh is the second person to go to sleep.
   C Jen goes to sleep at half past 12.
   D Aduke is very tired.

/ 3

Understanding the Language in the Text

Read the passage below, and then answer the questions that follow.
Underline the correct option for each question.

1   Tia trudged up the hill, the frosty grass crunching beneath her feet like sugar. Her
2 breath was a cloud in front of her face, making the distant trees hazy.

3   They had been on holiday for nearly a week now, and her only aim was to get some
4 good wildlife photos for her school project. Every day since they arrived she had been
5 up as soon as the weak winter sun struggled out of bed, determined to find the deer
6 that she knew lived nearby.

7   As Tia scrambled onto the rocky ridge, she gasped. There, so close that she could
8 almost touch them, was a whole herd of red deer!

Hint: *Read the text carefully before you start answering the questions.*

1. The author says that Tia's breath is a "cloud" (line 2). This shows that the weather is:
    A cloudy.   **B** sunny.   **C** cold.

2. Tia got up "as soon as the weak winter sun struggled out of bed" (line 5).
    This shows that Tia got up:
    A at sunrise.   **B** at sunset.   **C** while it was pitch-dark.

3. The author says that Tia "gasped" (line 7). Why do you think Tia does this?
    A She is surprised.   **B** She is out of breath.   **C** She is scared.

4. The author says that Tia could "almost touch" the deer (line 8).
    This shows that the deer:
    A have very soft fur.   **B** are very close to Tia.   **C** are very tame.

/ 4

Mixed Comprehension Questions

> Read the passage below, and then answer the questions that follow.

1   Anthea woke in the morning from a very real sort of dream, in which she was walking in the Zoological Gardens on a pouring wet day without any umbrella. The animals seemed desperately unhappy because of the rain, and were all growling gloomily. When she awoke, both the growling and the rain went on just

5 the same. The growling was the heavy regular breathing of her sister Jane, who had a slight cold and was still asleep. The rain fell in slow drops on to Anthea's face from the wet corner of a bath-towel which her brother Robert was gently squeezing the water out of, to wake her up, as he now explained.

    'Oh, drop it!' she said rather crossly; so he did, for he was not a brutal brother,

10 though very ingenious in apple-pie beds, booby-traps, original methods of awakening sleeping relatives, and the other little accomplishments which make home happy.

    'I had such a funny dream,' Anthea began.

    'So did I,' said Jane, wakening suddenly and without warning. 'I dreamed

15 we found a Sand-fairy in the gravel-pits, and it said it was a Sammyadd, and we might have a new wish every day, and –'

    'But that's what I dreamed,' said Robert.

From 'Five Children and It' by E. Nesbit

Turn over for the questions

Mixed Comprehension Questions

Answer these questions about the text on page 27.
Circle the letter of the correct option for each question.

1. What was the growling sound that Anthea heard when she woke up?
   A Jane snoring.
   B Jane blowing her nose.
   C Robert moaning.
   D Robert pretending to be an animal.

2. Which of the following things woke Anthea up?
   A The ceiling was leaking.
   B The rain was very noisy.
   C Robert was dripping water on her.
   D An animal was growling outside.

3. How do the three children know each other?
   A They are cousins.
   B They are brother and sisters.
   C They are friends.
   D They are at school together.

4. Where does Jane find the Sand-fairy in her dream?
   A In the zoo
   B In her bed
   C In a magical world
   D In the gravel-pits

/ 4

Mixed Comprehension Questions

Answer these questions about the text on page 27.
Circle the letter of the correct option for each question.

5. In her dream, what did Anthea think the animals were unhappy about?

    A They were getting wet.

    B They were tired.

    C They didn't have umbrellas.

    D They were hungry.

6. Which of these statements about Robert is not mentioned in the passage?

    A He's good at playing practical jokes on people.

    B He had the same dream as Jane.

    C He had the same dream as Anthea.

    D He was holding a towel.

7. What does the word "brutal" (line 9) mean?

    A Kind

    B Cruel

    C Rude

    D Funny

8. The writer says Jane woke up "without warning" (line 14). What does this mean?

    A She didn't tell anyone she was going to wake up.

    B She had been awake for a long time.

    C She hadn't shown any sign of waking up before.

    D She was still half asleep.

/ 4

Assessment Test 1

This book contains eight assessment tests, which get harder as you work through them to help you improve your Verbal Reasoning skills.

Allow 20 minutes to do each test and work as quickly and as carefully as you can.

You can print **multiple-choice answer sheets** for these questions from our website — go to www.cgplearning.co.uk/11+. If you'd prefer to answer the questions on the page, just follow the instructions in the question.

> Read this passage carefully and answer the questions that follow.

Recipe for Blackcurrant Ice Cream

You will need: 284 ml of whipping cream
4 eggs
100 g of caster sugar
3 tablespoons of blackcurrant juice

5   1) Separate the yolks from the egg whites and put them into different bowls. (Ask an adult to help you with this.)

2) Whisk the egg whites until they form stiff white peaks.

3) Add the sugar one teaspoon at a time while you continue to whisk the egg whites. The mixture will get stiffer as you do this.

10 4) In another bowl, whisk the cream until it is thick.

5) Add the cream to the egg white mixture.

6) Beat the egg yolks for a few seconds, and then add them to the egg white and cream mixture.

7) Add the blackcurrant juice and stir well.

15 8) Put the mixture into a plastic container and then put it in the freezer for at least 12 hours. (You can store it in the freezer for as long as any other ice cream — up to about 3 months.)

9) When you want to eat your ice cream, remove it from the freezer about ten minutes beforehand to make it easier to serve.

20 10) Serve with lots of fresh blackcurrants and berries.

Answer these questions about the text that you've just read.
Circle the letter that matches the correct answer.

1.   What kind of sugar do you need to make this ice cream?

A   Icing sugar
B   Caster sugar
C   Granulated sugar
D   Blackcurrant-flavoured sugar

2.   What is the first thing you must do to the eggs?

A   Put them in separate bowls
B   Whisk them until they form stiff peaks
C   Separate the egg whites from the yolks
D   Add sugar to them

3.   What happens when you whisk the sugar and the egg whites?

A   The mixture will become lumpy.
B   The mixture will become thinner.
C   The mixture will become firmer.
D   The mixture will become creamy.

4.   When should you add the blackcurrant juice?

A   Straight after separating the egg whites and yolks
B   Straight after adding the yolks to the cream and egg white mixture
C   Straight after whisking the cream
D   Before adding the sugar

/ 4

Carry on to the next question → →

5. What is the minimum amount of time the ice cream takes to freeze?

A   3 months
B   3 hours
C   12 hours
D   10 minutes

6. The ice cream will be easier to serve if you:

A   take it out of the freezer 12 hours earlier.
B   keep it in a plastic container.
C   put it in a bowl with plenty of fresh berries.
D   take it out of the freezer 10 minutes before you want to eat it.

7. What does the word "Beat" (line 12) mean?

A   Spread
B   Add
C   Measure
D   Mix

8. What does the word "beforehand" (line 19) mean?

A   Later
B   In plenty of time
C   Earlier
D   Ago

/ 4

> Fill in the missing letters to complete the words in the following passage.

9. Kai was so ex☐ited about his trip to the theatre

10. that he arrived half an hour e☐rly.

11. He took his seat and, as the minutes ti☐☐ed by,

12. he grew more and more ☐☐patient — when would Luke arrive?

13. As the li☐hts came up on stage,

14. Kai heard a huge crash b☐h☐nd him.

15. Luke had tried to creep q☐iet☐y to his seat,

16. but he had tri☐☐ed over an old lady's bag and he had gone flying!

/ 8

> Find the word that means the same, or nearly the same, as the word on the left.
>
> **Example: WET**   dry   <u>damp</u>   cold

17. **CUT**   hair   trim   knife

18. **TALK**   friend   word   chat

19. **HARD**   large   firm   soft

20. **LONG**   narrow   stretched   short

21. **SEARCH**   hunt   walk   treasure

22. **WRAP**   scissors   glue   bind

/ 6

Carry on to the next question → →

> Three of the words in each list are linked.
> Underline the word that is **not** related to the other three.
>
> **Example:** dress   skirt   <u>pink</u>   blouse

23. pie   muffin   apple   pasty

24. peaceful   deafening   silent   quiet

25. sorrow   sadness   misery   bliss

26. dragon   unicorn   human   ogre

27. paper   subtract   multiply   divide

28. midday   time   midnight   noon

29. squirrel   magpie   crow   eagle

/ 7

> Rearrange the words so that each sentence makes sense.
> Underline the word which doesn't fit into the sentence.
>
> **Example:** I <u>net</u> playing enjoy tennis

30. my pain is throat sore

31. her hair blonde wash is

32. I films watching enjoy actor

33. we to hometime go lessons

34. the was carpet muddy dirt

35. jungle in monkeys and the live

/ 6

Total   / 35

End of Test

Assessment Test 2

Allow 20 minutes to do this test and work as quickly and as carefully as you can.

You can print **multiple-choice answer sheets** for these questions from our website — go to www.cgplearning.co.uk/11+. If you'd prefer to answer the questions on the page, just follow the instructions in the question.

> Read this passage carefully and answer the questions that follow.

An Uneasy End to a Walk

Helen folded up her map and looked across the lake in despair. She and Jack were nearing the end of a long lakeside walk from their campsite. The long, hot afternoon was slowly turning cooler and they were tired. In the distance they could see the last ferry of the day. They had planned to catch it to travel back to
5 their campsite at the other end of the lake. If they missed it, they would have to walk all the way back. The walk had taken them several hours and if they had to retrace their steps, it would be dark before they returned. Yet the ferry still looked some way off.

"Come on, Helen," Jack urged her. "If we really hurry, we can manage this.
10 But we'll have to go without an ice cream."

"I don't mind that — so long as we get back!" replied Helen.

They started to run. It wasn't easy as they had rucksacks on their backs containing the remains of a picnic lunch, the map and their waterproofs. Every so often they would have to clamber over a rock or dash around a muddy puddle.
15 Neither of them dared to look at their watches; they just kept going.

As they rounded the final corner, they saw to their relief that the ferry was still at the jetty. They dashed towards it, Jack in the lead. As Helen's back foot touched the top step onto the ferry, the ferry attendant blew his whistle and locked the door behind them. They had made it with seconds to spare!

> Answer these questions about the text that you've just read.
> Circle the letter that matches the correct answer.

1. The walk in this story was:

   A up a mountain.
   B along a riverbank.
   C by a lake.
   D through a campsite.

2. When does this story take place?

   A In the morning
   B At lunchtime
   C In the dark
   D In the late afternoon

3. Why did Helen and Jack find it difficult to run?

   A They had forgotten their trainers.
   B Helen twisted her ankle.
   C They were carrying rucksacks.
   D The ground was slippery.

4. Which of the following did Helen and Jack not take on their walk?

   A Food
   B A map
   C Waterproof clothing
   D A picnic blanket

5. What did Helen and Jack try to avoid when they ran to catch the ferry?

   A Rocks
   B Puddles
   C Other people
   D Plants

/ 5

6. What happened at the end of the story?

A Helen and Jack missed the ferry.
B Helen fell over.
C Jack caught the ferry, but not Helen.
D They both caught the ferry.

7. What does the word "despair" (line 1) mean?

A Without hope
B Exhaustion
C Terror
D Triumph

8. What does the phrase "retrace their steps" (line 7) mean?

A Find a new route home
B Walk twice as far as they had before
C Walk back the way they had come
D Ask for directions

/ 3

The words in capitals are related in some way. Underline the word from the brackets that fits best with the words in capitals.

Example: PIG GOAT COW SHEEP (farm <u>chicken</u> milk meat)

---

9. APPLE ORANGE PEAR BANANA (fruit grape eat salad)

10. MATHS ENGLISH FRENCH HISTORY (school learn lesson geography)

11. THREE EIGHT SEVEN FIVE (ten number odd even)

12. CARROT TURNIP POTATO ONION (leek vegetable stew grow)

13. FOX BADGER WEASEL MOLE (ocean giraffe hedgehog animal)

14. SHIP BOAT BARGE YACHT (sail water canoe train)

15. SCREECH YELL SCREAM WAIL (noise whisper shout loud)

/ 7

Carry on to the next question → →

Assessment Test 2

Circle the letters next to the correct words to complete the passage below.

16. **A** seen
Last weekend, we went to **B** saw our new house.
  C see

17. **A** living
Whenever I see it, I get so excited about **B** thinking there.
  C leaving

18. **A** particular
The house is near the town centre, next to my **B** favourite restaurant.
  C tastiest

19. **A** hope
I **B** give that we will eat there all the time when we move!
  C view

20. **A** mine
I will have **B** my own room in the attic.
  C your

21. **A** tidy
I'm going to **B** fulfil it with posters and my paintings.
  C decorate

22. **A** to
The house that we're moving to has a garden and a terrace **B** two .
  C too

23. **A** space
The garden is really big, so there will be **B** time for a trampoline!
  C wish

/ 8

Complete the word on the right so that it means the opposite, or nearly the opposite, of the word on the left.

Example: big | s | m | a | l | l |

24. **sad** | j | | y | | u | l |

25. **hot** | c | | l | |

26. **little** | h | u | | e |

27. **always** | n | | v | | r |

28. **fair** | | | f | a | i | r |

29. **asleep** | | w | a | | e |

/ 6

Find the word that means the same, or nearly the same, as the word on the left.

Example: WET   dry   <u>damp</u>   cold

30. **RICH**   poor   wealthy   money

31. **JUMPER**   skirt   trousers   sweater

32. **MONEY**   cash   buy   purse

33. **TALE**   wag   story   read

34. **SAD**   cry   tears   miserable

35. **PAL**   enemy   friend   classmate

/ 6

Total   / 35

End of Test

Assessment Test 2

Assessment Test 3

Allow 20 minutes to do this test and work as quickly and as carefully as you can.

You can print **multiple-choice answer sheets** for these questions from our website — go to www.cgplearning.co.uk/11+. If you'd prefer to answer the questions on the page, just follow the instructions in the question.

> Read this passage carefully and answer the questions that follow.

First Snow

13 Cliff Road,
Summerton,
YO16 3HU
1st February

5   Dear Badal,

   I have missed you very much since I moved to live in England. Everything is new and different. I have so much to tell you!

   I was really excited by the thought of living close to the seaside and thought I would be able to play on the beach and swim in the sea every day. I was wrong!

10 Most of the time when we go to the beach it is so cold and windy that tears run down my cheeks. I wonder if it is ever hot in England.

   Anyway, you will never guess what happened. I couldn't believe my eyes when I woke up today and opened my curtains. The garden, trees and the roofs of the houses opposite were white and glittering! Dad said it is snow and Mum

15 made me wear so many clothes that I couldn't move my arms properly.

   I played with the children next door and had so much fun. We built a man out of snow and we sat on a sledge and raced down a hill near our house. Then we made balls from the snow and hurled them at each other. I will send you some photographs. I really wish you could see the snow.

20   Please write soon and tell me your news.

Love from,
Nisha

> Answer these questions about the text that you've just read.
> Circle the letter that matches the correct answer.

1. Which of these describes where Nisha lives?

    A Near the shops
    B On the beach
    C In the mountains
    D Near the sea

2. What did Nisha think she would do at the seaside?

    A Collect shells
    B Eat ice cream
    C Walk on the beach
    D Swim in the sea

3. What does Nisha notice about the temperature in her new country?

    A It is sometimes warm.
    B It is never cold.
    C It is very cold.
    D It is quite warm.

4. Why couldn't Nisha move her arms properly?

    A She hurt them when she was throwing snowballs.
    B They were so cold that they went stiff.
    C She had too many clothes on.
    D Her mum told her to keep them still.

/ 4

Carry on to the next question → →

5. Where did the children play on their sledges?

    A   On the road
    B   On a hill
    C   On the beach
    D   In the garden

6. Who did Nisha play with in the snow?

    A   Her dad
    B   Her sister
    C   The children next door
    D   Badal

7. What does the word "glittering" (line 14) mean?

    A   Sparkling
    B   Glowing
    C   Exciting
    D   Frightening

8. What does the phrase "I couldn't believe my eyes" (line 12) mean?

    A   I felt really worried.
    B   I was very surprised.
    C   I couldn't see properly.
    D   I thought it was a trick.

/ 4

Three of the words in each list are linked.
Underline the word that is **not** related to the other three.

Example: dress   skirt   <u>pink</u>   blouse

9. stone   kitten   rock   gravel

10. dentist   ogre   fairy   wizard

11. marmalade   butter   toast   jam

12. river   waterfall   stream   desert

13. yogurt   cake   chips   jelly

14. tree   sand   gravel   clay

15. touch   taste   soft   smell

/ 7

Fill in the missing letters to complete the words in the following passage.

16. The Bermuda Triangle is an ar☐a of the Atlantic Ocean

17. in which many mysteri☐☐s things have happened.

18. Several ships have vani☐h☐d without trace after sailing into the triangle,

19. while others have emerged from the area with all their crew missi☐☐.

20. Planes that have enter☐☐ the airspace above the triangle have also disappeared.

21. There are lots of theories about what caused these disappe☐☐ances,

22. ranging from bad w☐☐ther to alien abduction.

23. We may ne☐er know the truth!

/ 8

Carry on to the next question → →

Assessment Test 3

Rearrange the words so that each sentence makes sense.
Underline the word which doesn't fit into the sentence.

Example: I <u>net</u> playing enjoy tennis

24. he at works the popcorn cinema

25. I like jam toast on breakfast

26. fast time watch my is

27. most hutch carrots rabbits like

28. pantomime was the sing funny

29. Dana peanut wants jar butter

/ 6

Find the word that means the opposite, or nearly the opposite,
of the word on the left.

Example: BEAUTIFUL   nice   <u>ugly</u>   lovely

30. **WELL**	water	ill	healthy
31. **STOP**	fast	fail	move
32. **THIN**	long	skinny	fat
33. **END**	begin	bottom	arrive
34. **NEAT**	messy	clean	tidy
35. **TRUTH**	honest	lie	promise

/ 6

Total   / 35

End of Test

Assessment Test 4

Allow 20 minutes to do this test and work as quickly and as carefully as you can.

You can print **multiple-choice answer sheets** for these questions from our website — go to www.cgplearning.co.uk/11+. If you'd prefer to answer the questions on the page, just follow the instructions in the question.

> Read this passage carefully and answer the questions that follow.

A Faithful Friend

Long, long ago, in a land of mountains and valleys, a Prince went hunting in the woods. However, his faithful hound, who usually went with him, was left at the castle.

On his return, the Prince was greeted by his dog. However, the animal, who
5 was usually calm and quiet, was barking loudly. Alarmed, the Prince rushed to find his baby son who he had left sleeping upstairs. When he reached the room, the cot was overturned and the baby was nowhere to be seen. "You terrible beast!" the Prince roared. "What have you done?"

In his fury, the Prince instantly commanded his servant to seize the dog and
10 have it banished. The hound was taken away to a distant land where he could not harm the Prince's family again.

As the Prince sat and wept for his child and his lost companion, he thought he heard a baby's cry. Following the sound, the Prince discovered his child behind a cupboard, safe and unharmed. Close by lay the body of an enormous wolf
15 which had been killed by the Prince's faithful hound. In despair the Prince cried, "My good dog, you were protecting my son and yet I have forced you away."

Filled with regret, the Prince travelled to the faraway land where he had banished the dog. He searched for several days until he found the hound, and then brought him back to the palace where the dog protected the Prince and his son for
20 the rest of his life.

> Answer these questions about the text that you've just read.
> Circle the letter that matches the correct answer.

1. When did the Prince go out hunting?

   A A windy autumn day
   B Several years ago
   C A long time ago
   D Recently

2. What happened to the cot?

   A It was broken into pieces.
   B It was knocked over.
   C It was nowhere to be seen.
   D It was behind a cupboard.

3. Which word from the text tells you that the Prince was worried?

   A Alarmed
   B Commanded
   C Barking
   D Fury

4. Why was the dog taken away?

   A Because it had ruined the baby's room.
   B Because it had killed a wolf.
   C Because the Prince thought it had attacked the baby.
   D Because it hadn't gone hunting.

5. Why was the Prince "Filled with regret" (line 17)?

   A The dog had hurt the baby.
   B The dog was well-behaved.
   C The Prince realised he was wrong to blame the dog.
   D The Prince didn't want to punish the dog.

/ 5

6. Which word does not describe what the Prince's dog is like?

A Evil
B Brave
C Loyal
D Protective

7. What does the word "banished" (line 10) mean?

A Punished
B Sent away
C Locked up
D Killed

8. What does the word "companion" (line 12) mean?

A Child
B Friend
C Servant
D Helper

/ 3

Complete the word on the right so that it means the same,
or nearly the same, as the word on the left.

Example: tired [s][l][e][e][p][y]

9. **thin** [s][k][ ][ ][n][y]

10. **circle** [h][ ][ ][p]

11. **bag** [s][ ][ ][k]

12. **talent** [s][k][ ][ ][l]

13. **flexible** [ ][e][n][ ][y]

14. **scream** [s][h][r][ ][ ][k]

/ 6

Carry on to the next question → →

Assessment Test 4

Three of the words in each list are linked.
Underline the word that is **not** related to the other three.

Example: dress   skirt   <u>pink</u>   blouse

15. rocket   sun   moon   planet

16. apple   potato   banana   orange

17. piano   flute   violin   band

18. eagle   owl   robin   butterfly

19. football   netball   rugby   cycling

/ 5

The words in capitals are related in some way. Underline the word
from the brackets that fits best with the words in capitals.

Example: PIG GOAT COW SHEEP (farm <u>chicken</u> milk meat)

20. DRUM HARP OBOE TROMBONE (trumpet music instrument noise)

21. POND ROCKERY SHED LAWN (garden mountain greenhouse window)

22. GREEN YELLOW RED BLUE (paint colour orange bright)

23. BIT REINS HORSESHOE BRIDLE (saddle horse ride pony)

24. TRIANGLE SQUARE OVAL RECTANGLE (shape draw circle maths)

25. SILK LACE COTTON LEATHER (material clothes wool sew)

/ 6

Circle the letters next to the correct words to complete the passage below.

26. **A** go
Next weekend I am   **B** going   camping with my whole family:
   C gone

27. **A** me
   B mine   mum, sister, brother, aunt and grandad.
   C my

28. **A** sleeping
I usually enjoy   **B** breathing   in a tent and eating all my meals outside.
   C snoring

29. **A** pleasure
However, last time we went camping it was a   **B** disaster .
   C luxury

30. **A** ended
Firstly, it   **B** opened   raining as soon as we arrived,
   C started

31. **A** soaked
so by the time we'd put the tent up we were   **B** dry .
   C cosy

32. **A** fuel
Next, we ran out of   **B** eggs   for the camping stove and had to eat cold baked beans.
   C fire

33. **A** Firstly
   B Finally , my sister Laura was so frightened by a beetle
   C Evidently

34. **A** with
that she insisted on sleeping in my sleeping bag   **B** through   me!
   C unless

35. **A** event
Hopefully this   **B** one   we won't have so many problems!
   C time

/ 10

Total   /35

Assessment Test 5

Allow 20 minutes to do this test and work as quickly and as carefully as you can.

You can print **multiple-choice answer sheets** for these questions from our website — go to www.cgplearning.co.uk/11+. If you'd prefer to answer the questions on the page, just follow the instructions in the question.

> Read this passage carefully and answer the questions that follow.

Red Squirrels

Red squirrels, which used to be a common sight in Britain, are now becoming increasingly rare. They used to be the only species of squirrel in Europe, but since grey squirrels were brought over from America in the nineteenth century, there are now many more grey squirrels than red squirrels. In Britain, the
5 majority of red squirrels (about 120,000) can be found in Scotland, although there are around 15,000 in England and 3,000 in Wales.

Red squirrels in Britain mainly live in forests and they are well-adapted to living in the treetops, though in other parts of Europe they live in grassland and desert areas. They can grow to between 18 cm and 24 cm long, with a tail of up
10 to 20 cm which helps the squirrel to balance as it moves through the trees.

Red squirrels do not hibernate over winter, but they spend time in autumn storing food to keep up their strength during the colder months. They collect, and then bury, a wide variety of nuts and seeds. They also eat mushrooms and pine cones and, occasionally, birds' eggs.

15 The nest of a red squirrel is called a drey and is often built in the folds of a tree trunk. Baby squirrels are called kittens and are fed by their mothers until they are about 12 weeks old, when they develop their own teeth. Red squirrels usually live for about 3-6 years, but they can live longer in areas where there's lots of food available.

Answer these questions about the text that you've just read.
Circle the letter that matches the correct answer.

1. What are baby squirrels called?

A   Red squirrels
B   Kittens
C   Puppies
D   Dreys

2. What do squirrels usually do in autumn?

A   Sleep
B   Collect food
C   Make nests
D   Grow thick fur

3. What happens when baby squirrels are 12 weeks old?

A   They stop eating.
B   They leave the nest.
C   They grow teeth.
D   They can climb trees.

4. According to the passage, which of these do squirrels not eat?

A   Nuts
B   Pine cones
C   Berries
D   Eggs

5. What does the word "variety" (line 13) mean?

A   Range
B   Many
C   Group
D   Brand

6. What does the phrase "a common sight" (line 1) mean?

A   People liked to see red squirrels.
B   Red squirrels were often seen.
C   Red squirrels could see very well.
D   People found red squirrels boring.

/ 6

Carry on to the next question → →

Assessment Test 5

Read the passage carefully, then use it to answer the questions that follow. Circle the letter that matches the correct answer.

Karl peered out of the window of his living room. His best friend Eliza, her older brother Charlie and her cousin Ben should be here any minute. They were going to watch their local basketball team, the Bevington Bees, play arch-rivals the Atringham Adders.

Just then, Eliza jogged round the corner, wearing her stripy black and yellow Bees scarf. As Karl opened the door, she dashed inside, rubbing her hands together and stamping her feet.

"Hi Karl," she said. "Charlie and Ben are having a snowball fight — they'll be here in a minute. I had to leave them to it and get inside before I froze."

7. Which of these statements must be true?

A   Charlie and Ben are brothers.
B   Charlie is Karl's best friend.
C   Charlie is Ben's cousin.
D   Charlie is a fan of the Atringham Adders.

8. Why does Eliza rub her hands together as she comes inside?

A   She's excited about the match.
B   She's trying to warm them up.
C   She's brushing the snow off her hands.
D   It's a secret greeting between her and Karl.

/ 2

Find the word that means the opposite, or nearly the opposite, of the word on the left.

Example: BEAUTIFUL   nice   <u>ugly</u>   lovely

9. **DARK**   black   angry   pale

10. **FIX**   break   mend   fail

11. **JOY**   moan   comfort   sorrow

12. **LOSE**   steal   gain   jump

13. **TAKE**   gift   allow   give

14. **BUMPY**   smooth   uneven   empty

15. **TOP**   base   above   lower

16. **RESIST**   tempted   accept   fight

/ 8

Complete the word on the right so that it means the same, or nearly the same, as the word on the left.

Example: tired   s l e e p y

17. **light**   b ☐ i ☐ h t

18. **loud**   n ☐ ☐ s y

19. **vanish**   d i ☐ p p e a r

20. **windy**   ☐ r e ☐ z y

21. **flower**   b l ☐ ☐ m

22. **information**   k n ☐ ☐ l e d g e

23. **pursue**   f o ☐ l ☐ w

24. **tip**   h ☐ n ☐

/ 8

Carry on to the next question → →

Fill in the missing letters to complete the words in the following passage.

25. Last Sunday, I was in⬚⬚ted to Yousef's party.

26. His fami⬚⬚ live next door to mine,

27. so I could see the bright red bouncy castle in their ga⬚d⬚n from my window.

28. I was thri⬚⬚ed and couldn't wait to play on it!

29. Yousef's mum had made a delici⬚⬚s cake —

30. she had ⬚ritt⬚n 'Happy Birthday!' on it in icing.

31. We play⬚⬚ loads of games, like pass the parcel and musical chairs.

32. Yousef got loads of bri⬚⬚iant presents.

33. His aunt bought him a remote c⬚ntr⬚l car,

34. and he let us all have a go at dri⬚i⬚g it.

35. I had such a fan⬚as⬚ic time that I didn't want to leave!

/ 11

Total   /35

Assessment Test 6

Allow 20 minutes to do this test and work as quickly and as carefully as you can.

You can print **multiple-choice answer sheets** for these questions from our website — go to www.cgplearning.co.uk/11+. If you'd prefer to answer the questions on the page, just follow the instructions in the question.

> Read this poem carefully and answer the questions that follow.

An Extract from 'You Are Old, Father William'

"You are old, Father William," the young man said,
"And your hair has become very white;
And yet you incessantly* stand on your head —
Do you think, at your age, it is right?"

5 "In my youth," Father William replied to his son,
"I feared it might injure the brain;
But, now that I'm perfectly sure I have none,
Why, I do it again and again."

"You are old," said the youth, "as I mentioned before,
10 And have grown most uncommonly fat;
Yet you turned a back-somersault in at the door —
Pray, what is the reason of that?"

by Lewis Carroll

*incessantly — *continually*

Answer these questions about the text that you've just read.
Circle the letter that matches the correct answer.

1. Which of these descriptions best fits Father William?

   A Old, pale, fat
   B Young, white-haired, overweight
   C Old, white-haired, thin
   D Old, white-haired, overweight

2. According to the poem, how often does Father William stand on his head?

   A Sometimes
   B Over and over again
   C On his birthday
   D Every week

3. Why didn't Father William stand on his head when he was younger?

   A He didn't know how to.
   B He was frightened of being upside down.
   C He was so heavy that he fell over.
   D He was worried that he might injure himself.

4. Why is Father William confident that he can do headstands now?

   A He has practised a lot and can do perfect headstands.
   B He is old enough to know how to do headstands.
   C He injured his brain because he did so many headstands.
   D He isn't afraid of getting hurt because he thinks he doesn't have a brain.

5. Why is the young man surprised that Father William does somersaults?

   A Because Father William is fat.
   B Because Father William has white hair.
   C Because Father William has injured his brain.
   D Because Father William does headstands.

/ 5

6. What is the young man asking in line 12?

A Why Father William prays
B Why Father William does somersaults
C Why Father William is so old
D Why Father William is so strange

7. What does the word "replied" (line 5) mean?

A Asked
B Shouted
C Answered
D Laughed

8. What does the phrase "In my youth" (line 5) mean?

A In my childhood
B In my adult years
C When I was a baby
D When I was foolish

/ 3

Find the word that means the same, or nearly the same, as the word on the left.

Example: WET   dry   <u>damp</u>   cold

---

9. **SIGN**   notice   pinboard   draw

10. **HEAR**   talk   sound   listen

11. **RAY**   gloomy   beam   fire

12. **WOOD**   forest   tree   moor

13. **DASH**   wander   stroll   sprint

14. **MAKE**   create   factory   solve

/ 6

Carry on to the next question → →

Assessment Test 6

> Circle the letters next to the correct words to complete the passage below.

15. **A** to
From deserts to forests, and from fields   **B** from   your own back garden,
   C for

16. **A** over
ants are found all   **B** through   the world.
   C within

17. **A** most
Ants live in colonies with one or   **B** masses   females called queens,
   C more

18. **A** many
and   **B** lots   of male worker ants called drones.
   C some

19. **A** feeble
Some colonies also have strong 'soldier' ants with   **B** powerful   jaws,
   C broken

which are good for fighting.

20. **A** educated
Ants are very well   **B** loved   — they all have different jobs
   C organised

21. **A** diseased
to keep their colony safe, fed and   **B** healthy   .
   C sleepy

22. **A** build
They   **B** builds   large, complex nests using materials such as soil and leaves.
   C building

23. **A** ants
Underground nests consist of a number of   **B** drones   joined together by passages.
   C chambers

24. **A** and
They can be several metres deep   **B** so   many miles wide.
   C for

/ 10

Rearrange the words so that each sentence makes sense.
Underline the word which doesn't fit into the sentence.

Example: I <u>net</u> playing enjoy tennis

25. bought cat Sara a biggest

26. put are ornament that down

27. school to Pierre bike ran

28. dance hamster my anything eats

29. I in tomorrow the pond fell

/ 5

Complete the word on the right so that it means the opposite,
or nearly the opposite, of the word on the left.

Example: big s m a l l

30. **different** a l _ _ e

31. **most** l _ a _ t

32. **great** a w _ _ l

33. **play** w _ _ k

34. **sunny** r a _ _ y

35. **part** _ h o l _

/ 6

Total   / 35

End of Test

Assessment Test 6

Assessment Test 7

Allow 20 minutes to do this test and work as quickly and as carefully as you can.

You can print **multiple-choice answer sheets** for these questions from our website — go to www.cgplearning.co.uk/11+. If you'd prefer to answer the questions on the page, just follow the instructions in the question.

> Read this passage carefully and answer the questions that follow.

The Forest

Tariq decided that it was time to head back to the tent. He had turned around and was walking in the direction he'd come from, but the woods looked different now that it was growing dark. The tall black trees looked sinister, as if they had long, spindly arms stretching towards him.

5　　He began to run as fast as he could, but the trees clawed at his clothes, slapped his face, and tried to trip him up. Was that the wind he could hear in the trees, or was it something stalking him through the woods? He let out a small cry and rushed onwards, but suddenly there was nowhere left to run. Before him stood a line of bushes blocking his way forward. He was trapped!

10　　Panicking, he charged straight into the dense bushes. The branches and thorns tore at his clothes as if they were trying to prevent him from escaping. Tariq didn't give up. He fought and fought until, suddenly, he fell through to the other side and landed on the ground with a crash, bumping his elbow in the process.

　　"Hi, Tariq. Just in time. Dinner's nearly ready." Dad was standing ten

15　metres away, in front of the tent. He was wearing a ridiculous apron and holding a frying pan in his hand. Tariq didn't know whether to laugh or cry.

Answer these questions about the text that you've just read.
Circle the letter that matches the correct answer.

1. Why did the woods look different to Tariq when he was heading back to the tent?

   A   Because night was falling.
   B   Because he was lost.
   C   Because he was going back a different way.
   D   Because he was scared.

2. Which one of these does Tariq not do in the passage?

   A   Run
   B   Fall over
   C   Cry out
   D   Crawl

3. Why did the sound of the wind scare Tariq?

   A   He thought that he would be caught in a storm.
   B   He thought that it might be the sound of something following him.
   C   He thought it would whip the branches and thorns in his face.
   D   He thought the wind would blow the tent down.

4. How did Tariq react when he saw the dense bushes?

   A   He gave up because he was trapped.
   B   He looked along the bushes for a way through.
   C   He jumped over them and crashed to the ground.
   D   He forced his way through them.

/ 4

62

5. Which word best describes how Tariq returns to the campsite?

A Loudly
B Quietly
C Carefully
D Slowly

6. What does the word "dense" (line 10) mean?

A Thick
B Sharp
C Scratchy
D Twisted

7. What does the word "prevent" (line 11) mean?

A Help
B Stop
C Annoy
D Delay

8. What does the phrase "in the process" (line 13) mean?

A On the ground
B With great force
C In the same movement
D Just in time

/ 4

Fill in the missing letters to complete the words in the following passage.

9. It was a wild, st**o**rmy night in Little Haycombe.

10. In the sinister old house, perched high on the hillside ab**o**v**e** the town,

11. Professor Wormley cackled as he put the fin**i**s**h**ing touches to his invention.

12. "I'll show them!" he m**u**mbl**e**d to himself.

13. "They said that time travel wasn't po**ss**ible, but I know it is!"

14. With a final twist of the screwdriver, the time ma**ch**ine was ready.

15. Professor Wormley stood back to adm**i**r**e** his work.

16. At last, **h**oldi**n**g his breath, he flipped the 'on' switch.

/ 8

Complete the word on the right so that it means the same, or nearly the same, as the word on the left.

Example: tired s l e e p y

17. **coat** j a _ _ e t

18. **tired** _ _ h a u s t e d

19. **scared** f r i _ _ t e n e d

20. **sleep** s n o _ _ e

21. **lie** f _ b

/ 5

Carry on to the next question → →

> Three of the words in each list are linked.
> Underline the word that is **not** related to the other three.
>
> **Example:** dress   skirt   <u>pink</u>   blouse

22. beans   bread   crisps   chocolate

23. leaf   lawn   root   bark

24. leg   finger   heart   foot

25. roller coaster   candyfloss   dodgems   Ferris wheel

26. cottage   apartment   stable   house

27. lime   orange   lemon   apple

28. lion   zebra   panther   leopard

29. sneeze   cough   ill   sniff

/ 8

> The words in capitals are related in some way. Underline the word
> from the brackets that fits best with the words in capitals.
>
> **Example:** PIG GOAT COW SHEEP (farm <u>chicken</u> milk meat)

30. LAMB PIGLET KITTEN FOAL (sheep animal young puppy)

31. BURGLAR THIEF SWINDLER CONMAN (prisoner robber bad police)

32. LEAFLET BOOK RECIPE MAGAZINE (read study fiction newspaper)

33. POODLE COLLIE LABRADOR ALSATIAN (dog spaniel puppy train)

34. SWEDEN FRANCE IRELAND JAPAN (London country Italy city)

35. LOVE ADORE PRIZE TREASURE (cherish hate take gift)

/ 6

Total   / 35

End of Test

Assessment Test 8

Allow 20 minutes to do this test and work as quickly and as carefully as you can.

You can print **multiple-choice answer sheets** for these questions from our website — go to www.cgplearning.co.uk/11+. If you'd prefer to answer the questions on the page, just follow the instructions in the question.

> Read this passage carefully and answer the questions that follow.

The Roman Empire

The world has seen many empires rise and fall, but the most famous of all was the Roman Empire. Founded in Italy, the Roman Empire existed about 2000 years ago, and at its peak controlled the lands from western Europe to northern Africa, as well as parts of Asia and the Middle East. This meant that everyone
5   who lived in a country which was part of the Roman Empire had to obey Roman laws. Even as the Roman Empire grew bigger, Rome remained the capital city and it was there that many emperors lived.

One of the reasons the Roman Empire was able to defeat so many countries was the fact that it had a strong, organised army. Roman soldiers served in the
10   army for 25 years, so they were experienced warriors. They also had lots of equipment like helmets, shields and spears, so they were well prepared for battle.

However, the Romans were famous for more than just their fighting skills. They were also talented builders who built bridges, baths, theatres and temples in the countries that they invaded. They even linked their Empire with a road
15   network which allowed them to transport soldiers and goods quickly and directly. Today, there are plenty of Roman ruins still standing which remind us how powerful the Roman Empire was.

Answer these questions about the text that you've just read.
Circle the letter that matches the correct answer.

1. According to the text, who had to obey Roman laws?

A All Roman soldiers
B Everyone living in Rome
C Everyone in the Roman Empire
D Everyone living in Italy

2. According to the text, which of the following was not built by the Romans?

A Bridges
B Places of worship
C Roads
D Markets

3. According to the text, which of the following best describes Roman roads?

A Narrow
B Confusing
C Direct
D Long

4. According to the text, which of the following was not part of the Roman Empire?

A The Middle East
B Parts of Asia
C South Africa
D Western Europe

5. What does the word "talented" (line 13) mean?

A Rich
B Wise
C Honest
D Skilful

6. What does the phrase "at its peak" (line 3) mean?

A At its most powerful
B At its tallest
C At its richest
D At its busiest

/ 6

Circle the letters next to the correct words to complete the passage below.

After you leave school, it can seem
7. **A** trouble
    B difficult to learn new skills.
    C serious

However, there are lots of
8. **A** options
    B problems for grown-ups who want to learn.
    C motions

Evening classes are available in many towns and
9. **A** cities
    B islands ,
    C areas

and
10. **A** covering
     B cover   a range of subjects from carpentry to learning a new language.
     C covered

Many older people find that learning a new skill helps to keep them
11. **A** bored
     B friendly ,
     C active

while for others it can even open up new job
12. **A** fortunes
     B opportunities.
     C titles

13. **A** Although
     B However   , going to an evening class can be a great way to meet new friends.
     C In addition

So
14. **A** whether
     B whatever people want to learn to draw, rewire their home
     C how

or even
15. **A** like
     B write a bestselling book, there's bound to be an evening class
     C meet

that
16. **A** can
     B cannot help them on their way!
     C did

/ 10

Carry on to the next question → →

Find the word that means the same, or nearly the same, as the word on the left.

Example: WET   dry   <u>damp</u>   cold

17. **STRONG**   frail   mighty   shaky

18. **BRAVE**   bold   loud   angry

19. **POOR**   sad   needy   dying

20. **STRETCH**   long   leap   expand

21. **SCRIBBLE**   scrawl   scratch   script

22. **SHAVE**   bald   shear   scissors

23. **COMPLETE** mainly   partial   total

24. **ANGLE**   slant   ramp   straight

25. **SQUEEZE**   push   squash   tight

/ 9

Complete the word on the right so that it means the opposite, or nearly the opposite, of the word on the left.

Example: big   s m a l l

26. **lazy**   a c ☐ ☐ v e

27. **worse**   b ☐ t ☐ e r

28. **wild**   t ☐ m ☐

29. **back**   f ☐ ☐ w a r d

30. **clever**   ☐ t u ☐ i d

31. **funny**   s e r ☐ o ☐ s

32. **fall**   r i ☐ ☐

33. **climb**   ☐ e s c ☐ n d

/ 8

Assessment Test 8

Read the passage carefully, then use it to answer the questions that follow. Circle the letter that matches the correct answer.

Harriet had been looking forward to the school fair for months. She was helping on the tombola, and the clay vase she had made in class was going to have pride of place on the display of Year 3 artwork.

The day of the fair dawned bright and warm. Harriet had to be at school by half past nine, and she was out of bed and dressed before her dad came to wake her. At 9 o'clock her best friend, Jade, called for her and they walked the fifteen minutes to school together.

At 10 o'clock everyone started to arrive. The tombola was a huge success — there was a queue of people for it all morning, and it raised £130. The raffle raised £10 less than the tombola, while the cake stall made £60. By the end of the fair Harriet was exhausted, but she was delighted that they had raised so much money for new sports equipment for the school.

34. Which of these statements cannot be true?

A It was a sunny day.
B Harriet was late for the fair.
C The fair was on a Saturday.
D Jade is in Year 4.

35. Which of these statements must be true?

A Jade was working on the cake stall.
B The fair raised more than £300.
C The money raised by the fair went to charity.
D The fair raised less than £200.

/ 2

Total   / 35

End of Test

Assessment Test 8

Glossary

adjective	A word that <u>describes</u> a <u>noun</u>, e.g. '<u>beautiful</u> morning', '<u>frosty</u> lawn'.
adverb	A word that <u>describes</u> a <u>verb</u>, which often ends with the <u>suffix</u> '<u>-ly</u>', e.g. 'She laughed <u>happily</u>.', 'He ran <u>quickly</u>.'
antonym	A word that has the <u>opposite meaning</u> to another, e.g. an antonym of 'good' is 'bad'.
connective	A word that <u>joins</u> two sentences or parts of a sentence, e.g. '<u>and</u>', '<u>but</u>', '<u>because</u>'.
consonants	The <u>21 letters</u> of the alphabet that <u>aren't vowels</u>.
fiction	Text that has been <u>made up</u> by the author, usually about <u>imaginary people</u> and <u>events</u>.
homophones	Words that <u>sound the same</u>, but mean different things, e.g. '<u>hair</u>' and '<u>hare</u>'.
imagery	Language that creates a <u>vivid picture</u> in the reader's mind.
multiple choice	A type of <u>11+ question</u> that gives you <u>answers</u> to choose from.
non-fiction	Text that is about <u>facts</u> and <u>real people</u> and <u>events</u>.
noun	A word that <u>names</u> something, e.g. '<u>Paul</u>', '<u>cat</u>', '<u>fear</u>', '<u>love</u>'.
prefix	Letters that can be put <u>in front</u> of a word to <u>change its meaning</u>, e.g. '<u>un-</u>' can be added to '<u>lock</u>' to make '<u>unlock</u>'.
pronoun	Words that can be used <u>instead</u> of <u>nouns</u>, e.g. '<u>I</u>', '<u>you</u>', '<u>he</u>', '<u>it</u>'.
suffix	Letters that can be put <u>after</u> a word to <u>change its meaning</u>, e.g. '<u>-er</u>' can be added to the end of '<u>play</u>' to make '<u>player</u>'.
synonym	A word with a <u>similar meaning</u> to another word, e.g. '<u>big</u>' is a synonym of '<u>huge</u>'.
verb	An <u>action</u> or <u>doing</u> word, e.g. '<u>run</u>', '<u>went</u>', '<u>think</u>', or a <u>being</u> word, e.g. '<u>is</u>'.
vowels	The letters '<u>a</u>', '<u>e</u>', '<u>i</u>', '<u>o</u>' and '<u>u</u>'.